My House

by **Kelly Gaffney**

illustrated by Ed Myer

Here is my house.
This is the gate.

3

Here is my house.
This is the garden.

5

Here is my house.
This is the roof.

6

Here is my house.
This is the door.

Here is my house.
This is the hall.

11

Here is my house.
This is the kitchen.

13

Here is my house.
This is the bathroom.

Here is my house.
This is the bedroom.